Enchanted Kingdoms

Rosalind Kerven

BRITISH MUSEUM PRESS

Rosalind Kerven is a trained anthropologist who now works as a full-time writer and reviewer of children's books. She has published numerous volumes of myths, legends and folk-tales as well as children's novels.

© Rosalind Kerven 1997

Rosalind Kerven has asserted her right to be identified as the Author of this work

Published in 1997 by British Museum Press
A division of The British Museum Company Ltd
46 Bloomsbury Street, London WC1B 3QQ

A catalogue record for this book is available from the British Library

ISBN 0 7141 2105 3

Designed by Carla Turchini
Printed in Slovenia

Consultant: Susan Youngs

Cover: Detail from folio 124r of the Book of Kells (see page 46).

Contents

About these stories

About 2,500 years ago, in the Iron Age, Celtic peoples lived in many parts of Europe. They were split into numerous different tribes, each one having its own king, queen or chief but sharing the same Celtic languages and laws. They were farmers and proud warriors, and although they did not read or write, they were very skilled at craftwork and followed a complex religion.

The Iron Age peoples did not call themselves 'Celts', but used their own tribal names. The name 'Celts' was given to the native peoples of Britain and Ireland by scholars, hundreds of years later.

The stories in this book belong to the Celtic-speakers of Ireland, who are the direct ancestors of many modern Irish people. Some Irish myths describe the adventures of the old Celtic gods and goddesses. Others are supposed to explain the history of ancient Ireland – though the events and characters described are often much too extraordinary to be true.

The two stories here are about the legendary Irish warrior Finn and his son Oisin. Finn is described as a hero from pre-Christian times. He led the Fianna, a noble group of warriors, who dedicated themselves to protecting the High King of Ireland against enemies and invaders. The Fianna were a very special group: young men who wished to join them had to prove their strength and bravery by surviving various difficult and dangerous ordeals. Once they had been accepted they had to follow a strict code of behaviour. Finn himself was a kind of superman, who could always overcome monstrous enemies by his cunning and supernatural strength, and who had the gift of seeing into the future.

For many centuries the stories about the Fianna were remembered and passed on simply by being told out loud.

Details were added to the stories over the years. They were first written down in Old Irish about 800 years ago, in the Middle Ages.

Some aspects of these stories have been kept alive in more modern Irish fairy tales. The tradition of magic spells, of giants and fairies, of romantic kings, queens and princesses, of an enchanted 'other-world', and of the good hero triumphing over evil – all have their roots in ancient Celtic myths.

How to Say the Names

Most of the names in this book are not difficult. A few might be hard if you are not used to Irish names:

Finn mac Cumhaill   FIN MAC COOL
The Leader of the Fianna

Oisin   U-ZINE
Finn's son

Niamh   NEEVE
Princess of Tir na n'Og

The Magic Drinking Horn

They were telling stories one winter's night long, long ago, in the meeting house of the village. The old woman Glanlua stepped forward from the shadows into the flickering red light of the fire. A dreamy look came into her eyes as she cleared her throat; a hush fell, and she began:

You've all heard of Finn mac Cumhaill, haven't you? You know how he defended the green realm of Ireland, how he defeated every enemy and monster that dared to threaten the High King? Oh, he was a real hero, was Finn: all the young men used to be lining up to join his war-band – the Fianna they were called – but only the very strongest, cleverest and noblest in all the land would do!

Well, listen to this: he was every bit as wonderful as the stories say, was Finn – and I ought to know because I met him once.

This Celtic gold coin shows a warrior mounted on his horse.

Most Celtic men were brave and skilful fighters; even farmers were expected to be ready to leave their fields at any time if their king called them to go to war.

However, for Finn and the Fianna, fighting was a full-time job. Like all Celtic warriors, they were carefully trained in the skills and rituals of battle, and they were expected to be strong and courageous.

1 The Enchanted Mist

It was many years ago, when I was not much more than a girl, and only newly married. I was riding over the mountains of Fuad with Lavaran, my husband. It was a golden summer's day when we first set out, but as we followed the path up to the higher slopes, we noticed a change come into the air; the birds suddenly fell silent and everything grew unnaturally still. Then, the next thing we knew, we were lost – smothered in a great white cloud of swirling mist.

We both jumped from our horses. It was eerie and very scary, so when we heard a familiar sound a short way off, we both sighed with relief.

'Those are hunting horns,' I said, 'and dogs barking. There must be a party of huntsmen somewhere close by. Maybe they could guide us safely off the mountain.'

'I'll go and ask them for help,' said Lavaran. 'You wait here.' And before I could stop him, he was gone.

I wasn't very happy about being left there all alone, but he'd vanished into the mist, I didn't know in which direction, so I had no choice but to wait. The horses weren't happy either. They were stamping their hooves and snorting, for the mist had an evil smell to it; and then they jerked the reins right out of my hands and bolted away.

I couldn't stand it any longer, stranded all alone in that dreadful spot, with the silence crowding in on me. I began to creep away, treading gingerly through the sucking patches of foul-smelling bog and tangled brambles, and all the while I was calling 'Lavaran! Lavaran! Where are you?'

I don't remember how long this went on before suddenly my heart leaped like a deer, because another voice answered me back: 'Who is it, who's there?' It was a man's voice, but it certainly wasn't Lavaran. I didn't know whether to be relieved or afraid.

As I stood there, a shape came out of the mist, and another one behind it. They stepped forward and I saw two huntsmen, both tall and well-dressed, and heavily armed. They seemed so formidable that I began to back away, but the first man called out to me to wait.

Horses were much admired for their strength, beauty and courage, and were often used as a symbol of great warriors such as the Fianna. They were ridden in battle or used to pull war-chariots.

Most ordinary Celtic men and women were probably skilled riders, for horses and horse-drawn wagons were the only quick way of travelling long distances over land.

This small bronze horse-mask may have been nailed to a vehicle as a decoration.

As I hesitated, his eyes ran shrewdly over me; then he bowed to me and held out his hand in a friendly way. I stole a glance at his face, and my knees turned to water, for I guessed at once who he might be.

His deepset eyes were green and fearless; his hair and moustache were the colour of ripe wheat; his whole body rippled with the calm, easy strength of a bull. When he spoke, his voice was warm and mellow, like polished oak.

'My dear lady!' he said, as if I were a noblewoman rather than a common, mud-spattered farm-girl, 'whatever are you doing, caught up in this enchantment? It certainly wasn't meant for you.'

I couldn't think how to answer these strange words. 'Enchantment?' I stuttered back at him. 'What do you mean?'

'This mist is a trap,' said he. 'I'm pretty sure it's been set by an evil magician to catch me and my men.'

'A ... a trap, sir?' I said. 'But why? Who's set it?'

He laughed easily, as if this were an everyday matter, no more than a joke. 'I don't know yet, my lady; I've so many enemies!'

I must have looked astonished, for he added confidingly, 'They all hate me, you see, because they know I'm stronger and more cunning than the lot of them put together. They can play the dirtiest tricks they want, but no one will ever get the better of mighty Finn mac Cumhaill!'

So I'd guessed right! I can tell you, as soon as he spoke his legendary name, my heart turned right over.

'Sir,' I whispered, 'I am very honoured to meet you.'

'No, no,' he cried, with a smile that sent a thousand butterflies racing through my heart, 'the honour is not yours but mine! Nothing gives me greater pleasure than to help a beautiful woman out of trouble.'

Then, with gentle words, he calmed me down and made me tell him my name, where I had come from, where I was going, and how I had lost Lavaran.

'Glanlua,' he repeated, storing my name carefully in his memory, 'dear lady, I feel so bad about all this. Innocent people like you shouldn't have to get mixed up in warriors' feuds. Now, if you will allow us, I promise we will do all we can to help you and guide you to safety before things take a turn for the worse.'

'Sir,' I answered, 'I'd be so grateful if you could only lead me back to my husband.'

Finn nodded, then introduced me to his companion. 'This is Dara,' he said, 'a trusted friend of mine – and also a brilliant musician. Take his arm, Glanlua, and hold tightly on to him as you pick your way across the bog. He's as strong as a rock, and he won't let you fall. I shall go in front, and try to find a straight path.'

So we set off like this, and all the while, Finn and Dara were doing their best to chase away my terror by the brightness of their talk.

'I expect you're wondering how this business started,' said Dara. 'Well, Glanlua, we don't yet know the roots of it, but the day began strangely as soon as our band set out hunting, for we found ourselves chasing the most extraordinary deer.'

'We should have guessed it was no ordinary animal,' Finn called back to me. 'It was too exquisitely shaped, absolutely enormous, whiter than the moon, and even the wind couldn't keep up when it ran.'

This bronze figure of a dog is probably a deer-hound, a common hunting breed. It was made in Britain after the Romans invaded.

Hunting was a very popular sport for Celtic warriors and kings. They usually chased after deer or wild boar. Dogs were vital to help the huntsmen track down and kill their prey. Fierce watchdogs also protected herds of cattle. Many stories mention faithful hounds.

'The truth is,' said Dara, 'that we did guess it was some kind of enchantment – but that only made the chase more thrilling! Besides, if any man had urged us to let it go, Finn here would have branded him a coward, and forced him to leave the Fianna.' He paused to swing me easily over a stretch of black, treacherous mud. 'Anyway, after several hours' hard riding after it, the creature vanished into thin air. Meanwhile, all our men were scattered, right across the whole mountain. And the next thing we knew, this mist came rising out of the ground and wrapped itself around us like a death-shroud.'

Ahead of us, suddenly Finn stopped. 'The mist hasn't done us any real harm yet,' he said, 'but the next thing might. Listen.'

I couldn't hear anything at first. Then, out of the silence, weird music came drifting towards us, painfully sweet, unearthly, haunting. As it passed over, I clapped my hands over my ears to block it out, but that made no difference. For the music was already seeping deeply into me like a powerful poison, making my head spin and my limbs all weak and helpless.

'There's no fighting this, Finn,' Dara murmured.

Swaying, I stared at Finn in disbelief, but to my dismay he only shook his head.

'But sir,' I cried, 'you told me yourself – no one can beat mighty Finn mac Cumhaill!'

'Not in battle,' he said, 'but this is different.' His wonderful deep voice had become slow and hoarse. 'What you can hear, Glanlua, is fairy music. The enemy must be allied to the hidden people of the hills. There is no resisting their bewitchments.' A great sadness and weariness was spreading over his handsome face. 'I am so sorry.'

The misty world around me seemed to be spinning ever faster: all three of us were swaying helplessly with the music. Louder and sweeter it grew, flooding right through the very core of our beings. And then at last we all sank slowly to the ground, and fell into a deep, deep sleep.

2 The Giant's Castle

I don't know how long we slept, but when at last I awoke, Finn and Dara were still beside me. The mist had completely cleared, and the sun was shining brightly. We were no longer on the upper slopes of the mountain. Somehow we had found our way down into a pleasant valley, and were lying on a grassy bank that sloped to the shores of a calm, blue lake. Just across the water and directly opposite, there stood a magnificent castle.

We all sat up and rubbed our eyes. I could see that Finn and Dara were feeling as I was, heavy-limbed and fuzzy headed. Every movement seemed slower than usual. We stared about us at the unfamiliar landscape. Then suddenly Dara said in a thick voice,

'We've been spotted! Someone is coming from the castle.'

Sure enough, the great door was swinging open. Out of it came two people, a woman and a man who towered monstrously above her, for he was a giant. They walked briskly down to the shore; then, without bothering to undress, both plunged straight into the water and swam across. When they reached our bank they climbed out and, still dripping, strode towards us. She had the cultured air of a noblewoman, but the giant looked rough and sinister even though he was wearing the gold torc of a powerful chief.

I turned desperately to Finn and Dara, expecting that both would draw their swords and destroy the giant before he could touch us. But to my great horror, I realised that the heroes were still virtually paralysed.

The giant loomed over us with an ugly snort. Then he squatted down and grabbed hold of Finn and Dara, one in each huge, dirty hand. He didn't actually touch me, but I shrivelled under his pitiless gaze.

'So!' he roared, 'if it isn't brave Finn mac Cumhaill, chief groveller to the King! Got you at last! There's rumours everywhere about you: they say you're quite a little warrior. Aren't you going to fight me then? Go on, Finn, hit me, punch me, poke your tiny sword at me! Ho ho, ha ha, I'm not afraid!'

In ancient times, rich and powerful Celtic men wore beautifully-made torcs. A torc is a thick metal collar or neck-ring. This torc was made of gold, but some were bronze or iron. Books written by the ancient Romans describe how Celtic warriors went into battle 'adorned with gold necklaces and bracelets'.

Archaeologists have found many torcs in ancient graves and also in buried hoards of precious metal. This one was found in 1950 by a Norfolk farmer ploughing his field. It is about 2,000 years old.

You'd think that Finn would have exploded with anger at such mockery; but instead he looked calmly back into the giant's ugly face and said dryly, 'Didn't your mother ever tell you, giant, that it's terrible bad manners to threaten a man when he's in no position to fight you back? Besides, you haven't even told me your name yet, or what your quarrel with me is about.'

'Dryantore's my name,' rasped the giant, 'and I've got you into my power, Finn, so I can take revenge on you for killing my two sons. This good lady with me is my sister Ailna, and the revenge is on her behalf, too, since you also killed her husband.'

'Did I?' said Finn. 'When?'

'After the battle of Knockanare,' said the giant, 'and everyone knows that your side only won it by cheating and foul play.'

'Ah yes, I remember that battle, Dryantore,' Finn said. 'The King of Ireland asked me to defend him against a brutish army that was all ready to seize his realm. Plenty of my men died then, too, but the only reason we finally won it was through our skill in honest fighting.'

'Don't get cheeky with me, midget!' roared the giant. 'Don't you dare to argue! All I care about is that my sons and my brother-in-law are all dead because of you – and we're going to punish you so that it really hurts!'

Then he pulled some rope from his belt and used it to tie all three of us up, while Ailna stood by, giggling and shouting crude instructions. One by one, he picked us up and hurled us across the lake; then the evil pair swam across after us, grabbed us by the hair, dragged us into the castle and threw us into the dungeons.

3 Dara's Music

We lay there a long, long while in total darkness. The stone floor was hard and cold, infested by scurrying spiders and rats.

I could not stop myself from bursting into tears. Finn heard and found enough strength to crawl over to comfort me. 'Glanlua,' he said, 'be brave! The game's only just started. I've met villains like Dryantore before: most of them are as stupid as they are evil, and I've always beaten them in the end.'

Still, as yet there was nothing even he could do except sit and wait. Nothing relieved the boredom or the fear. No food was brought to soften our hunger, no drink was offered to take the edge off our thirst. What with that, and the spell of dream-like weakness that was still on us all, I thought it wouldn't be long until we died.

But we didn't. For after countless hours had passed, the dungeon door heaved open and there, standing in a dim shaft of light, was the giant's sister Ailna. She looked first at Finn and Dara with pure hatred in her eyes, and then she turned to me.

'Stupid girl!' she hissed. 'Fancy spending your time with wretches like these two!'

In the darkness, I felt Finn and Dara willing droplets of

courage into my own fearful heart. I took a deep breath and answered in as steady a voice as I could, 'If you wish to know the truth, madam, I never set eyes on either of these good gentlemen before yesterday; and I never would have done, if it wasn't for the enchanted mist you and your brother put on the mountain.'

Ailna took her time to consider this. 'If that's so,' she said at last, 'I suppose we ought to set you free. Let me go and ask my brother what he thinks.' She slammed the dungeon door shut and disappeared, only to return a while later with the horrible Dryantore beside her. He said not a word, but reached into the dungeon and snatched me roughly out, as if I were a trapped bird he was bringing from a cage.

I was already feeling queasy from the enchantment, and the smell of that unwashed giant so close made me faint again. I was only half aware of him carrying me up a long, winding staircase to the castle's main hall, where he put me roughly on a couch. There Ailna offered me food, but I was much too ill to take it.

Through my swoon, I heard the pair of them arguing.

'She needs the magic drinking horn,' said Ailna.

'Rubbish!' snapped the giant. 'That would be a complete waste of its powers.'

'Don't be mean, brother,' said Ailna. 'We've no quarrel with her, have we?'

She got her way in the end. The drinking horn they'd spoken of was brought to me and its end put into my mouth. I couldn't tell you what drink was in it: something sweet and cool, and as soon as it passed down my throat, I felt the strength rushing back into my body, and the colour coming back into my cheeks. I sat up, took the food that Ailna held out to me, and ate it as fast as I could. By the time I'd finished, I felt much better.

I'll say this for Ailna: she wasn't quite as vicious as her brother. In fact, after that she acted fairly friendly, showing me around the castle and displaying all her jewels and treasures. But she refused to let me go free, and when I mentioned Finn and Dara she flew into a rage.

'It's terribly cruel to leave them down in that dungeon,' I said. 'They're almost dying from hunger and thirst.'

A bronze mirror
like this could have been among the treasures that Ailna
showed off to Glanlua. One side was highly polished so
that its owner could see her reflection; the other side was
beautifully decorated.

Mirrors have been found in the graves of Celtic women in
Britain and Europe. This mirror was made in England in the
first century BC.

Celtic stories describe women as very beautiful – and often
very vain! They bathed every day, fashioned their long hair into
elaborate styles, and wore make-up.

'Nothing's cruel enough for that murderer Finn!' she shrieked at me. But then she looked thoughtful. 'Dying did you say? Hmm. I don't think Dryantore wants them dead just yet. His plan is to keep them both alive for a while longer. He means to use them as decoys, to lure the rest of the Fianna to the castle. Then he'll lock the whole lot of them in the dungeon so that they can all starve to death together!'

'Oh!' I said. 'But it'll never work unless you give Finn and Dara some food and drink pretty soon, because I'm sure that by now they must be very close to death.'

She saw the sense of that and went hurrying away to tell her precious brother.

'Arrch,' he rumbled, 'what a nuisance! I suppose we'd better feed them just a measly bit.' So he swaggered down to the dungeon with a plate of dry crusts and a couple of bowls filled with murky river water, with Ailna and me trailing along behind. Poor Finn and Dara were fed and watered just like dogs. Then, when they were a bit recovered, he began to taunt them again, holding up his huge fists, and challenging Finn to fight.

'I'll fight you all right,' said Finn, 'Just as soon as you lift this spell off me.'

Dryantore roared with laughter. Then he turned to Dara. 'What about you, toad?' he sneered. 'I've heard that you're something of a musician. Go on then, play a pretty little ditty for me!'

'No,' said Dara.

But Finn said, 'Why not, my friend? It would cheer us all up to hear a tune.'

Of course, no member of the Fianna ever dared to argue against Finn. I heard the rustle of cloth and leather, as Dara unfastened something from his belt. Then suddenly the clear, honeyed note of a flute burst into the rank dungeon air.

I cannot tell you how lovely it was – different in every way to the creepy fairy music of yesterday. Oh, it was bursting with sweetness and dawn-light, full of brilliant glory and hope, enough to uplift the darkest soul.

'More!' barked Dryantore when Dara paused.

Ailna threw him another crust of bread, and he played again. But no sooner was this second tune finished than Dryantore was rocking with evil laughter. 'Well done, Dara – you've set a trap for your cronies, just as I wanted! I've worked a simple spell to make sure this music of yours can be heard from here right across the mountain. All your silly friends are still out there searching for the two of you. They'll recognise your tune and be able to work out exactly where you are. Then they'll come running along here, like moths to a flame – and I'll be able to destroy all the Fianna at once!'

Dara's flute may have been made from a sheep's bone, like this ancient pipe.

Music and dance were important to the Celts. We know that ancient Celts played the lyre, pan-pipes and kettle drum, and used a special type of trumpet to frighten the enemy when they went to war. (The horseman on the coin on page 9 is holding one – you can just see it.)

4 Things Turn Very Nasty

Dryantore slammed the dungeon door shut, yelling at Ailna and me to follow him up the steps. Back in the hall, the two of them pushed me aside, then went secretively into a corner where they muttered strange, foreign-sounding words and mixed up something steaming in a large cauldron.

From outside, we heard a scurry of footsteps and shouting. The Fianna had arrived! But this noise did not last long: suddenly there came a loud 'thud' as if many bodies were falling together to the ground. Then everything became uncannily silent. At this, Dryantore drew his sword from its scabbard, seized another coil of rope and rushed out excitedly, with Ailna close behind.

I crept after them and peeped through the door. There, on the grass in front of the palace, I saw the most dreadful scene. A hundred or more strong, handsome men were lying stricken on the ground – not dead, but seemingly turned to stone, their glassy eyes staring helplessly at the sky, their lips working

A fighting man wore his sword at his side in a metal scabbard, which hung from a chain or leather belt around his waist. This decorated scabbard was found in Ireland.

Celtic swords were made of iron, beautifully crafted, with very sharp edges. The hilt (handle) was often made of bronze and bone, and decorated with engraving or coloured glass.

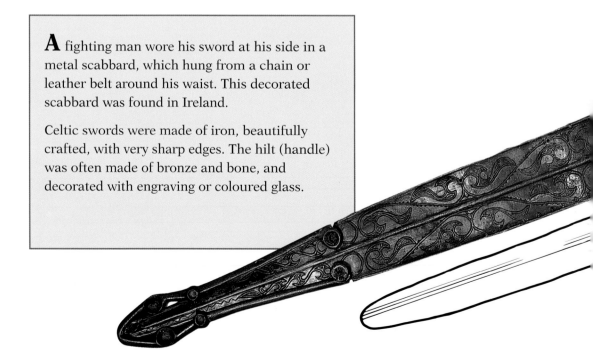

soundlessly. Dryantore stomped gloatingly amongst them, stopping to tie each man up with his rope.

But I never saw any more, for suddenly I heard a movement behind me, and then someone whispered my name. My heart jumped and I swung round. There, creeping like a fox from the shadows of another door, was Lavaran!

We fell into each others' arms. But just as we started to tell each other all about our extraordinary adventures, Ailna bustled back in. Lavaran slipped away – but not quickly enough.

'Dryantore!' she called, 'you've missed one!'

The giant put his enormous head round the main door and grinned. Then he set off where Ailna pointed, through the winding passages of the castle, his great nose sniffing the air like a dog on the scent.

It didn't take long before he was back, dragging Lavaran behind him. They paused by the cauldron, where I saw Lavaran suddenly turn stony stiff like the others. Then the giant pushed him roughly down the steps into the dark, filthy horrors of the dungeon.

Dryantore came leaping back, laughing heartily. 'I've got them all, I've got them all!' he shouted.

'What are you going to do with them?' Ailna asked him.

'I had planned just to starve them to death,' he said cheerfully, 'but now I've thought of something more fun. What I'll do is go down there every day with my sword and chop some of their heads off, just a few at a time.'

A little while later, he went down and started his disgusting game.

'That was really satisfying!' he said, when he came upstairs afterwards. 'Why don't you come and watch it next time, ladies?'

I couldn't even bear to think about it, let alone see it, but Ailna forced me to go down with her. We stood together by the door while Dryantore unlocked it and flung it open. It was very dark inside, but in the thin beam of the giant's oil-lamp, I saw to my relief that Lavaran was still alive, as were both Finn and Dara. It was awful to see how broken these fine men had become, lying there writhing helplessly.

Dryantore swaggered down the steps, brandishing his sword as he stepped into the shadows.

Suddenly one of the men screamed, 'NO! Not me! Please don't kill me, giant!'

'What's the matter, coward?' Dryantore roared back at the screamer. 'I thought the Fianna were all supposed to be big, brave boys. What are you afraid of? Want your mummy, do you?'

Out of the darkness the voice said hoarsely, 'Death, that's all. I'm not afraid of anything except my own death.'

And then I recognised Finn's voice, deep and unmistakably commanding: 'Hold your tongue, Conan! You're a disgrace to all the Fianna.'

'Conan, is it?' chortled the giant. 'Well, Conan, you know I've got you pinned to the spot, don't you? Oh ho, watch out then: I'm coming for you ... coming to get you ... NOW!'

'Stop!' shrieked Conan. 'Listen, Dryantore, if you spare my life I'll do anything for you. I promise, I swear it, I'll swap sides – leave the Fianna, turn my back on Finn mac Cumhaill. I'll come to work for you ... I'll be your faithful servant!'

'A servant!' roared the giant. 'Well, that's a fine idea, isn't it, Ailna? I've always fancied a servant!'

'Don't be an idiot, brother!' she hissed at him. 'He's one of the enemy. You can't possibly trust him.'

'Stop worrying,' chuckled Dryantore. 'Join in the fun! You heard with your own ears – he's going to join our side. Anyway, Finn and all the rest of his pathetic men will all be dead within a few days.'

He snapped his fingers at Conan who, suddenly finding himself free to move, stood up and stumbled to the bottom of

High-born people drank wine or mead (an alcoholic drink made from honey) from a drinking-horn instead of a cup. They used an animal horn, with fine metal fittings to protect the end. This bird-headed metal terminal (tip) was found at Lismore in Ireland in the Middle Ages. The animal horn has rotted away over the years.

The old stories tell how important guests were welcomed with a drink served in a horn. The lady of the house usually handed the horn around.

For ordinary everyday use, most people drank beer from wooden pots.

the steps to meet us.

'Come on,' roared the giant. 'Come and join me, just like this young lady did!' He slapped me on the back, then pushed us both to the hall in front of him.

As we went, Conan whispered urgently in my ear: 'Glanlua: I beg you to help us!'

'Of course!' I whispered back. My mind was racing. When Dryantore came up behind us I took a deep breath, then said, 'Sir, forgive me for speaking, but this man won't be much use as a servant while he's still weak from your spells.'

'That's true,' said Dryantore.

'So perhaps you should let him have a sip of that magic drinking horn you gave to me?' I said.

'No!' cried Ailna. 'It'll be the death of us if any of the Fianna get hold of that!'

'Why do you keep making problems, woman?' Dryantore grumbled. 'It's no use having a servant who's too weak to work, is it? Just do what the little lady's so sensibly suggested. Go and fetch me the magic drinking horn.'

Ailna threw me an angry look, but she got the horn and let Conan drink from it, just the same.

5 The Last Battle

Conan stood up. He flexed his muscles. Then he dropped his hands back to his side, so that one of them nudged meaningfully against me. I saw him eyeing the magic horn again, and then the dungeon steps. I tried to work out what he wanted me to do; and suddenly I had a fine idea.

'Oh,' I cried. 'I can hear music! Just listen to how lovely it is! It must be Dara playing his flute again.'

'I can't hear anything,' said Dryantore.

'You need to go a little closer,' I said.

Dryantore went to the top of the dungeon steps to listen. So did Ailna.

From the corner of my eye, I saw Conan snatch up the magic drinking horn, and hide it under his cloak.

'It seems to have stopped,' I said.

'Brimstones!' growled Dryantore. 'I really enjoyed that fellow's music. I'd like to hear it once more, before 1 finish killing them all off. I'm going to go down there and force him to play another one for me. Cheer up Ailna: I'll let you choose the tune.'

They hurried down the steps. Conan and I followed close behind.

As Dryantore unlocked the heavy dungeon door, Conan nudged me again and pointed, first at the bump concealed under his cloak, then up to the hall.

I nodded and said, 'Ailna, you don't mind me mentioning it, I hope – but did you remember to put the magic drinking horn away?'

Ailna clapped her hand to her mouth. 'I clean forgot!' she said. 'Oh Dryantore – someone might steal it if we're not more careful, and then we'll be in real trouble!'

'Fool!' cried the giant. 'I'd better come too, to make sure you put it somewhere safe.'

He grabbed her wrist and pulled her back past us – leaving the dungeon door swinging wide open. Conan and I wasted no time, but hurried straight in.

'Friends!' called Conan in a loud whisper, 'we bring you freedom!' He swept the drinking horn out of his cloak.

A bearded Pictish warrior on horseback drinks from his horn. Its bird-headed terminal is looking back at him. The Picts were Celtic peoples of north Britain. They have left many lovely stone carvings like this.
(You can see another one on page 33.)

'One drink from this magic vessel will restore all your strength. Finn, my lord: let the first taste be for you!'

He held the horn to Finn's parched lips and poured the magic liquid down his throat. Almost at once, the leader of the Fianna jumped up, restored to all his handsome glory. He gave a shout of pure joy, and passed the horn on to the next man.

But at that very moment, the shaft of light that shone through the open door was blacked out. Giant Dryantore had come back!

'Cheats!' he roared. 'Swindlers! Give me back my drinking horn!'

Before Conan could answer, Finn had leaped forward and stood brandishing his sword up at the giant's face.

'How dare you accuse my warriors of cheating?' he bellowed. 'It's you who are the dishonest one, Dryantore – trapping us by devious spells and evil magic. Weren't you brave enough to fight me like an honest man? Well, here we are now, face to face at last, on an equal footing. I challenge you: face me and fight me properly!'

'No, brother!' Ailna screamed.

But Dryantore, foaming at the mouth, was already drawing his own sword.

'Stand back, ladies,' commanded Finn.

I shrunk away, almost tumbling over a huddle of men who were eagerly awaiting their turn for a drink from the magic horn. It was passed around quickly, and as each man revived, he jumped up and stood ready in case he was needed to join in the battle.

Dryantore was bigger than ten strong men, and his strength was greater than twenty mad bulls. But the Fianna had greater skill in fighting, and they also had right on their side. Before long, the giant was in retreat.

He fled backwards, up the winding steps and across the hall, while Finn came leaping after him. Now Dryantore gathered speed, and it looked as if he might escape.

'A spear!' yelled Finn. At once one of his men was beside him, pressing a spear into his hand. Finn took aim and threw it. Whistling through the air it went, gliding more smoothly than a bird, until it reached Dryantore and pierced his heart.

With a shriek, the giant fell to the ground and died.

Now the Fianna all let out a great cheer. They came swarming out of the dungeon, strong and free.

'The brute's sister is dead too,' Conan called. 'She collapsed and died of fright.'

I felt a pang of sadness at this news, for Ailna had been quite kind to me despite her villainy; in fact, tears came to my eyes. But Finn came over and said, 'My dear Glanlua, you mustn't cry at this happy moment! Look, here's your husband back, safe and sound. Didn't I promise you everything would end well? And just think: the Fianna have survived largely thanks to you.'

Then he turned and shouted to his men: 'Come, my friends, let's raid the defeated enemies' kitchen and give ourselves a well-earned party!'

The spearhead which killed Dryantore could have looked like this, though perhaps not so finely decorated. This one is made of iron with elegant bronze patterns riveted to the blade. Because it is so beautifully made, archaeologists think a great chieftain may have carried it during ceremonies or celebrations, over 2,000 years ago.

Spears were important weapons which could be used from horseback or from a chariot. Some Celtic spears had handles up to 2.5 m long.

So Finn's men went all over the giant's castle, and soon found more delicious food and wine than Lavaran or I had ever dreamed of. They spread it out like a banquet, in bowls of gold and cups of silver, and then we all ate and drank to our heart's content.

After that, Dara got out his flute and began to play some tunes that were so quick and cheerful, none of us could help ourselves: we had to get up and dance. Because I was the only lady there, every one of the Fianna took his turn to dance with me, and Lavaran was proud to let them; but I have to say, no man I ever met could dance as well as their leader, the noble Finn mac Cumhaill.

By the time the merriment was over, I was more than weary: I leaned against Lavaran's shoulder and fell fast asleep.

When at last I woke, it was early morning, and Lavaran and I were all alone. The giant's castle and the lake were gone; and Finn and the Fianna had all vanished away, just like the enchanted mist.

The Land Beyond The Sunset

An old, old man came hobbling slowly along the road. His hair and beard were like tangles of white, wispy cobwebs, hanging to his knees. His face was deeply etched with wrinkles, his back was bent almost double; he squinted through sunken, clouded eyes. He really was extraordinarily ancient – no wonder everyone stopped to stare at him!

Gasping for breath, he sat down to rest upon a large, grey stone. The people watching crept a little closer.

'Come on then,' he croaked, 'don't hang back! I know you're all wondering about me. Well, I don't mind telling my story, if there's any of you curious enough to listen ... '

1 The Woman From The Sea

My name is Oisin; and my father was none other than that mighty hero, Finn mac Cumhaill! Oh, I can tell you all think I'm making that up: Finn's been dead for hundreds of years, hasn't he? But if you'll just keep quiet while I explain what happened, you'll soon understand the truth.

Yes, I reckon I must be more than 300 years old! Finn really was my father; and Finn was also my lord. For in my youth, when I was strong and handsome, I was a member of his famous warrior band, the Fianna; and wherever he led I always followed, whether it was to fight or to play.

Well, one fine spring morning when there were no enemies for us to deal with, Finn led us all out on a hunting expedition. The forests were simply teeming with deer in those days, and we rode after them for miles and miles, over the hills and through the forests, until we found ourselves by the sea.

The stag we'd been chasing had completely disappeared. We went all over the beach looking for it, but it was nowhere to be seen. Then suddenly one of the men shouted, 'Look at the water!' We all turned to stare. The grey waves seemed to fall apart, and the next moment, a huge white horse with golden hooves came rising out, and on its back was a woman.

Oh, if only you could have seen her! Her long, loose hair fell heavily over her shoulders like spun gold. She was wearing a flowing dress of dark red linen and a long cloak. The sunlight was flashing and dazzling off her brooches and bracelets. As she came closer, I saw that her eyes were deep blue, touched with the calm of twilight.

She was the most beautiful woman in the whole world – more beautiful than you can imagine. She came galloping past all the other men, heading straight for me.

When she reached me, she reined in her horse, but she didn't dismount. I was completely lost for words, but my father strode up to her and challenged her in his usual severe manner.

'Greetings princess! I am Finn mac Cumhaill, leader of the High King's warriors. Now then: tell me your own name, what you want with us, and whether we should regard you as an enemy or a friend.'

She smiled down at him and answered, 'Greetings, Finn! I am delighted to meet you, for you are very famous even in my own distant home. But I haven't travelled all this way to find you, sir. My name is Niamh of the Golden Hair, and the man I want is this one – Oisin, your son.'

Her voice was sweeter than a bird's when she spoke my name. I gazed into the blue depths of her eyes, and there was nothing I could do to stop myself from turning weak with love.

'My son?' Finn said sharply. 'What do you want with him?'

'I want to marry him,' she said. 'I want to take him home with me, back to my own country, which is the land of perfect happiness, far across the sea, way beyond the sunset.'

'What is this country's name?' demanded Finn.

'It is Tir na n'Og,' said she, 'and my father is its king.'

'Tir na n'Og !' I cried. 'I've heard of that place. The poets say that it's an enchanted kingdom, where all the people live for ever and never grow old.'

This Pictish carving shows a grand lady (like Niamh) riding side-saddle, with a hunting party. Can you spot the fine brooch which fastens her cloak? You can see a brooch on page 34.

Celtic women had the reputation of being proud, brave and strong-minded. Although the Celts considered men to be more important, high-born women had plenty of freedom and power. Some women even went to war alongside their men. Wives and husbands were fairly equal partners in a marriage. When a king died, his wife sometimes continued ruling as a queen in her own right.

Still smiling, she answered, 'Everything the poets say about my country is quite true, Oisin – only it is even more wonderful than they could dream of.' She leant down and took my hands in hers, which were very soft and white. 'In Tir na n'Og we feast every day on honey cakes, roast venison, and rich red wine. Our robes are soft and rich, our beds are filled with goose-down, our treasure chests are overflowing with silver and gold.

High-born ladies owned valuable jewellery – but probably not whole treasure-chests of it, unlike the princess of Tir na n'Og! This brooch comes from the great royal site of Tara in Ireland. It is made of silver, some parts covered with a thin layer of gold, and the stone is amber. Important men and women wore brooches to fasten their cloaks – men at the shoulder, women on the chest.

Poorer women, like Glanlua in the first story, might have worn simple pins of bone or bronze instead of rich brooches.

If you come to live there as my husband, you shall have a sword of purest silver that never grows blunt. You can hunt all day, then dance with me every night to the music of fairy harps. Now listen, Oisin: I must tell you that I have had countless offers of marriage in the past; many chiefs, princes, and even kings have begged me to become their wife, but I refused them all. For I have often dreamed about you, and I believe that you are much braver and more clever, much more noble and handsome than any of them.'

I was bewitched by her. My heart was melting fast, like snow under the warm April sun. I didn't know what to do.

I forced myself to turn away, and in a whisper, I begged Finn for advice. I was startled to see his proud eyes shining with tears. 'If you go with her, my son,' he said quietly, 'you and I will never meet again. But even so, you must follow your own heart.' And with those words, he walked off and left her and me, face to face, alone.

Niamh laughed and said, 'Oh Oisin, the look in your eyes is enough to tell me that you already love me! Well then, I shall place you under a *geis*, a sacred promise. I bind you to my side, Oisin, I bind you to ride with me all the way to Tir na n'Og. I bind you to become my husband.'

There was only one way a man could escape such a *geis*, and that was through death. But if I went with her to Tir na n'Og, I could avoid death for ever! So I said, 'I am proud and happy to be bound to you, Princess Niamh.'

Then I went to my father, and said farewell. I bowed to all my comrades and called my goodbyes to them. They answered me with the three dark shouts that were a signal of deepest grief. This reminded me of my father's last words but there was nothing I could do about it, for a *geis* may not be broken.

'Come,' said Niamh.

I swung myself up onto the great white horse behind her. Almost at once it broke into a flowing gallop, and then we entered the sea.

2 Rescuing A Queen

Oh, it was a huge thing, that horse: a dream of muscles and speed. It flew over the waves, it raced with the wind, and all the time it kept us both dry and safe, steady as a rock in a storm.

We passed many islands. Some were rich with woods and pastures, while on others stood magnificent marble cities. Animals raced across the sea before us: huge stags and nimble spotted fawns; and once a white dog with red ears. A little boat, made of pure, beaten gold, sailed across our path: a young woman was sitting inside it, pulling at the golden oars. After her came a mounted warrior in a cloak of yellow and carrying a golden sword. I was astonished by all these sights; but Niamh only laughed and said, 'you haven't seen anything yet, Oisin – just wait until you reach my own enchanted country!'

Night fell and the next day dawned, and still the white horse carried us steadily westward. As the sun rose behind us, we came to a small, bleak island on which nothing grew and nothing was built, except for a palace above a curving beach of bone-white sand. Our horse rose from the waves and ran across the sand, and when we came to the palace gate, it stopped.

This wasn't the enchanted land I had imagined!

'Have we arrived?' I asked Niamh. 'Is this palace yours?'

She didn't answer, but knocked three times upon a gate. Almost at once it swung open and behind it I saw an elegant but very sad-looking young woman, wearing the robe and crown of a queen.

'Good morning,' she said.

'Good morning,' said Princess Niamh. 'Are you the daughter of the King of the Land of Life?'

'I am,' she answered, 'but it's been many years since I last saw my father. An evil giant has stolen me away, and now he forces me to live here all alone with him as his prisoner.'

'So I've heard,' said Niamh, 'and it's a dreadful thing that's happened to you! That's why we stopped here, as we were passing by. This fine young man is going to be my husband. His name is Oisin and he belongs to the Fianna, that famous war-band from Ireland. If anyone could set you free, it's him.'

The young queen's tear-soaked eyes lit up with sudden hope. 'Well,' she said, 'if that's so, you are certainly both most welcome! Please come in, come in.' Then she led us inside to the main hall of her palace, where she seated us on golden chairs, and offered us dish after dish of delicious food washed down

Oisin was astonished to pass a gold rowing boat as he and Niamh raced across the sea. This beautiful model boat from Ireland is only about 20 centimetres long. It is real gold. It was probably made for a religious ceremony.

In real life the Celts made boats called **coracles** of wood, or wood and leather.

by huge drinking horns full to the brim with a honey-sweet drink.

I ate and drank heartily, for I was very hungry after our long journey. When I was finished, I thanked her profusely and said, 'Now, please tell me your story, madam, and explain to me how I can help you.'

'Well,' she said, 'my story is both short and tragic. I grew up happily enough in my father's palace. But one day, a really vicious, foul-mouthed giant came stalking there – Fomor of the Blows, they call him – and as soon as he saw me, he snatched me away and locked me up here in this lonely wasteland.'

'Did he force you to marry him?' I asked her.

'No,' she said, 'luckily he couldn't. For, terrified as I was, I kept my wits about me, and I managed to bind him to a *geis*, a sacred bond. "I'll never marry you," I said, "until I see you prove yourself by fighting and beating a champion warrior face to face." He laughed at that, thinking it would be an easy condition to fulfil – but he was wrong. For he's so big and fierce, this Fomor, that not one man has ever dared come forward to take up the challenge.'

'Well,' I said, 'I would be delighted to tackle him.'

'I'm sure you would,' said she, 'but Oisin, I must beg you this – please don't fight him unless you're absolutely certain that you can win. For if you lose, by the terms of our *geis*, my fate will be sealed and I'll have to become his wife and stay with him for ever.'

'There's no danger of that,' I assured her.

She looked rather worried, but we had no time to discuss it further, for the next minute, the door burst open – and in walked Giant Fomor himself!

He was a huge, ugly, loathsome fellow, with a messy bundle of fresh-killed deer on his back, and a great iron club in his hand. He scowled at his queen and leered at Niamh. Then he threw the deer into a corner, turned to me and shouted in a rough, booming voice: 'What do you want here, fish-face? Get out of my palace at once before I bash your brains in!'

Well, you must have heard how we Fianna were afraid of no-one.

'I've come to fight you, villain!' I shouted back at him. 'I've come to settle the *geis* that this young queen here has put on you!' Then I drew my sword, gripped my shield and stood before him, and the next minute our fight began.

Though it was only between him and me, it wasn't a quick battle, nor was it an easy one. We fought for one day, we fought for two, we fought for three whole days and nights; but still neither of us was the winner. We fought without food or drink, and we didn't stop once to rest; but still, neither of us was the loser. In all the wars and battles I'd experienced since I joined the Fianna, I'd never met an enemy even half as terrible as him.

Most Celtic warriors in early times did not wear body armour – in fact it was said that some stripped naked for battle. Fighters protected themselves from sword blows with oval, round or rectangular shields.

Shields were made of wood, covered in leather for extra strength. This one is fronted with bronze panels, very finely decorated. It is so ornate that it was probably used for ceremonial occasions, not for battle. It was found in the River Thames in London. The owner probably threw it into the river deliberately, as a splendid gift to the gods.

At last I grew so weak and weary that it seemed I was going to fail. I thought wretchedly of how that poor young queen would have to marry this brute, and I thought of Finn, my father and how ashamed of me he would be. Neither of these thoughts was of any help. But then I saw Niamh of the Golden Hair watching me, and remembered how she'd said I was far better than any chief, prince, or king in all the world – and in one final burst of strength, I swung my sword so hard that it cut off the giant's head in one clean sweep!

At this, the two women leaped foreward with a cry of joy. I myself was half-dead from my wounds and fainted into their arms. They put me to bed, and brought me ointments and medicines made from magic healing herbs, so that soon my strength returned. Then I went out and dug a deep grave for the giant, right in the middle of his windswept island, and marked it with a sombre pile of hard, grey stones.

'That's a good job well done,' said Niamh, 'and it was a fine treat for me, Oisin, to see that you're even braver and stronger than I thought! But now we must hurry along on our way.'

So, saying goodbye to the queen (who was already preparing to return to the Land of Life), we both jumped back onto the great white horse with the golden hooves, and set off again across the sea.

We galloped and flew, skimming the waves, chasing the wind, passing many more wondrous sights. We flew into the heart of a storm, pounding with the thunder, swirling with the gale, then out again and beyond, on and on and on.

At last we came to a place where the sunset itself rose up before us – a glowing curtain of gold and crimson fire. We passed straight through it. On the other side, a new country shimmered out of the sea, touched with the soft light of rainbows.

Niamh turned her golden head to smile at me. 'A thousand welcomes, Oisin,' she said. 'We're home.'

3 Tir na n'Og

As we rode up the beach, we were greeted by a troop of warriors wearing horned helmets and brightly coloured armour, marching to the music of trumpets and drums.

Behind them came a procession of young noblewomen and men; and at their head were the queen and king.

I stared at these monarchs in amazement: I knew that they were the mother and father of Niamh – yet neither of them looked a day older than she was!

The king met my stare with a stately bow, saying, 'Welcome, noble Oisin son of Finn, welcome to Tir na n'Og! We look forward to you marrying our daughter. We know you will enjoy every day that you live here, for this realm is an enchanted one where everyone stays young for ever, and every day is a festival.'

In the story, the warriors who greeted Niamh and Oisin when they arrived in Tir na n'Og wore special horned helmets. In ancient times, bronze helmets with 'horns' were probably used for ceremonies, not for war. Battle helmets would have been made of iron, which is stronger.

Like the shield on page 39, this helmet was thrown into the River Thames as a religious sacrifice, or gift.

Then he led us into his palace where a great banquet had been prepared. For ten whole days and nights we ate, drank, danced, sang, and listened to storyteller-poets, without ever feeling tired; and at the end of that time, the lovely Niamh and I were married.

After that, for a long, long time I was perfectly happy. Each day melted sweetly into the next, and each hour was filled with even better things than the last, so that I lost all track of time.

But one day, as I sat under a sun-dappled tree, I fell to day-dreaming. My mind was flooded with memories of my old life, and tears came into my eyes.

'What's the matter?' Niamh asked me.

I didn't want to trouble her, but in Tir na n'Og dark secrets are not allowed, so I could not help but answer, 'I'm thinking of my father, Finn, and my old comrades in the Fianna, and the rainwashed hills of Ireland. I'm wishing that I could see them all again.'

'If you do want to go home, I cannot stop you,' said Niamh slowly. 'However, I would strongly advise you against it. Listen, Oisin: if you return to Ireland, you will be in the most terrible danger. There is only one way to avoid it: all the time you are there, you must stay on the back of my magic horse. Do not dismount; do not let even one foot touch the ground, for even one second. For if you do, you and I will never see each other again, and all the great happiness there is between us will be lost.'

I listened to her carefully, and though I could not understand the reason for it, I promised to heed her warning.

'But even so,' she said, 'it would be better if you did not go, for you will never find your father, nor any of your comrades in the Fianna.'

'Surely that can't be true?' I said, 'it's hardly any time since I left them.'

'Don't you understand, Oisin?' she persisted. 'Here in Tir na n'Og, where everything is perfect, time hardly passes and nothing ever changes. But across the wide ocean in Ireland there are such things as death and grief.'

But I was suddenly yearning for my old home.

'I must go,' I told her, 'but I promise I will be careful, I promise I will come back.'

She said not another word, but took me to the stable where the white horse with golden hooves was waiting: she saddled it and whispered in its ear, then watched silently as I mounted it.

Almost at once, the horse began to gallop towards the shore. I had just one last quick glance at Niamh, her beautiful blue eyes shining with unaccustomed tears; and then I was flying homewards over the wide, wide ocean.

4 The Strangest Things Of All

The journey was just like the first one, racing night and day over the waves, passing many astonishing sights, until at last we came to the green land of Ireland.

I was very weary and longed to find a soft bed to rest in, but remembering Niamh's warning I dared not get down from the horse. So I stayed astride it and rode on, but as I did, my heart became filled with fear and gloom.

Ireland had changed. Nothing was as I remembered it. The villages I used to ride through every week had been deserted and fallen into ruin; while strange new houses had been built in places that had always been empty before. Even worse, I didn't recognise any of the people who came out to stare as I passed: they all looked shrunken and unfamiliar.

At last I stopped at a farm and, leaning from the horse, asked the farmer outright, 'Tell me, is Finn mac Cumhaill still alive? And do the Fianna still protect the High King?'

He shot me a very odd look as if I were mad. 'Finn mac Cumhaill?' he cried, trying to suppress a fit of laughter, 'where have you been hiding, young man? It must be about three hundred years since that old legend was around!'

Three hundred years! Yet it seemed more like only three months that I had spent in Tir na n'Og.

But of course, I thought, in Tir na n'Og no one ever grows old, no one ever dies. In Tir na n'Og time does not pass according to the normal rules. No wonder Niamh had warned me that I would be disappointed if I came home!

With a heavy heart, I rode on to the place where I had

When Oisin came back to Ireland he found only ruins of the places he had known. These round hillocks are man-made earthworks, all that remains of the great royal centre of Tara in Ireland.

The earthworks are really very ancient, older than the stories and the other objects in this book. People in Ireland gave it the name 'Tara' later on, imagining that such a grand site could have been the royal court. It is very difficult to be sure of things and places from centuries ago! Archaeologists have to study the evidence very carefully to try to find out the truth.

grown up. Finn had built a fine, big house there, but nothing was left of it except a crumbling heap of stones, covered in grass and weeds.

I decided to return to Tir na n'Og as fast as I could. I turned the white horse and urged it towards the sea.

But before I could reach the shore, I found the road blocked by a group of men who were shouting and arguing over an enormous stone. They jumped in front of me, signalling me to stop.

'Hey, stranger,' called their leader, 'you look like a big, strong fellow. Can you help us?'

'What's the problem?' I asked, for we Fianna were always glad for a chance to be helpful.

'We need to move this stone here,' he said, 'but even all of us together aren't strong enough to do it. Could you add your own muscle-power to ours?'

I looked down at the men more carefully. They were dwarfs compared to me.

'Of course,' I said. 'Just stand back. I might even be able to manage it by myself.' I was smiling at my own superior strength as I leaned down from the saddle, lifted the stone with one hand, and pushed it right out of the way.

The men watching let out a great cheer. I admit it: their admiration made me feel really good. But that was the last time I ever experienced such triumph. You see, as I stretched out to move the stone, the saddle girth broke. Now as I straightened up, it gave way, so that I lost my balance, began to slip ... and the next moment, I'd fallen right down and was standing on the solid ground of Ireland – the very thing that Niamh had warned me not to do!

It was the end of everything for me.

The great white horse shook itself, neighed – and vanished. As I stood there, raging against my own carelessness, my sight began to dim, then my hearing grew suddenly muffled. Even worse, I was shrinking and shrivelling! In those few dreadful minutes I grew terribly old, bent and twisted, weak and useless, just as you see me now.

So, my friends, now you must surely understand everything. I am so broken hearted! I will never return to the fabulous land of Tir na n'Og. Never again will I see my heroic father, Finn mac Cumhaill, nor any of my good friends in the Fianna.

But I'm not a selfish man. Most of all, I'm grieving for what has become of Ireland. I can hardly bear to see how the old gods are long forgotten, all the great heroes are dead, and there is hardly a drop of magic or glory left in all the land.

When Finn was alive, the Celts still followed their old, pagan religion and worshipped many gods and goddesses. But when Oisin returned to Ireland hundreds of years later, he found that these beliefs had been replaced by Christianity.

However, the old ideas were not completely forgotten over the years. This picture is in the Book of Kells, a medieval Irish manuscript of the Christian Gospels. (It was made in the 8th century AD – 1200 years ago.) The Book of Kells was written and decorated by Christian monks, but their love of fierce beasts and curving, interwoven decoration comes from the patterns used by pagan Celtic artists long before Ireland was Christian.

The old stories about the Fianna were still told, too – just as they are today.

Further Reading

For children
Mike Corbishley, *The Celts Activity Book*, British Museum
Press, 1989
Patricia Hansom, *British Museum Colouring Books: The Celts*,
British Museum Press, 1997
Robert Hull, *Stories from the British Isles*, Wayland, 1994
Gordon Jarvie, *Irish Folk and Fairy Tales*, Puffin, 1992

For adults
Miranda Green, *Celtic Myths*, British Museum Press, 1993
Miranda Green, *Dictionary of Celtic Myth and Legend*, Thames
and Hudson, 1992
Simon James, *Exploring the World of the Celts*, Thames and
Hudson, 1993
Simon James and Valery Rigby, *Britain and the Celtic Iron Age*,
British Museum Press, 1997
I. Stead, *Celtic Art*, British Museum Press, 1996 (revised
edition)

The Pictures

BM = Image used by courtesy of the Trustees of the British Museum, photo by British Museum Photographic Service